Invisible Ink

Barbara Mitchelhill

Published in association with
The Basic Skills Agency

Hodder & Stoughton
A MEMBER OF THE HODDER HEADLINE GROUP

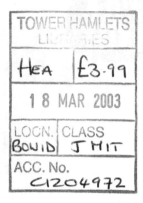
Acknowledgements
Cover: Lee Stinton
Illustrations: Jim Eldridge

Orders: please contact Bookpoint Ltd, 39 Milton Park, Abingdon, Oxon OX14 4TD. Telephone: (44) 01235 400414, Fax: (44) 01235 400454. Lines are open from 9.00–6.00, Monday to Saturday, with a 24 hour message answering service. Email address: orders@bookpoint.co.uk

British Library Cataloguing in Publication Data
A catalogue record for this title is available from The British Library

ISBN 0 340 74265 8

First published 1999
Impression number 10 9 8 7 6 5 4 3 2
Year   2004 2003 2002 2001 2000

Typeset by Fakenham Photosetting Ltd, Fakenham, Norfolk.
Printed in Great Britain for Hodder & Stoughton Educational, a division of Hodder Headline Plc, 338 Euston Road, London NW1 3BH by Athenaeum Press Ltd, Gateshead, Tyne & Wear.

Contents

1

They get to Bob

After a long day, Matthew was almost home.
He turned the steering wheel
and swung the car into Sandon Road.
'What the . . .?'
He slammed his foot on the brake and stared.
An ambulance was outside the flats,
its blue light flashing.

Matthew jumped out of the car
and ran down the street.
A group of people were standing. Watching.

Matthew looked over the heads of the crowd.

Two men in uniform walked out of Sandon House
carrying a stretcher.

When he saw who was on it, his heart began to pound.

'Oh no!' he said. 'It's Bob!'

He pushed his way through the crowd to the stretcher.

'What happened?' he asked.

The old man on the stretcher turned his head.

'They got to me in the end,' he whispered.

'Don't let them get to you. Don't give in.'

His eyes slid closed and his hand went limp.

'Leave him to us, sir,' the ambulance man said.

'He needs medical help.'

Matthew watched, stunned,

as they closed the ambulance doors and drove away.

This meant all the old tenants had been scared away.

He was the last. What would happen to him now?

2

Blood

Matthew felt sick with fear
as he pushed open the door of Sandon House.
The problems had started last December.
The building was sold
and the new landlord – whoever he was –
wanted them out.
He threatened them and they were scared.
Really scared.
Four tenants left as soon as they could.
Only Bob Jones and Matthew stayed.

'We can put up with it,' Bob had said
and Matthew agreed.

But then someone new moved into the top floor flat.
After that, things got much worse ... like today.
Seeing Bob on that stretcher was a shock.
What had they done to the old man?
What had he done to deserve it?

Matthew stepped inside the building.
Ugh! The stink! It was part of Sandon House now.
It didn't use to be.
He pinched his nostrils
and hurried down the hall to his flat.
Then he saw a large piece of paper pinned to the door:

He was angry and he tore it down.
'Get lost!' he said. 'I've had enough!'

He turned the key and stepped into the flat.
As he reached for the light switch,
he felt something slippery under his shoe.
His foot shot out from under him.
He lost his balance and landed hard on the floor.
'What the ...?'
He was lying in slime.
He could feel it on his hands.
The carpet must be covered with it.

He struggled to his feet and found the light switch.
He turned to look at the living room – and gasped.
'BLOOD!' he said.
'Somebody's covered the flat with blood!'
He tried to stop his head spinning.
Then he ran to the kitchen, clutching his stomach.
He leaned over the sink and was violently sick.

3

Matthew's Plan

The next day at the factory,
Matthew told his boss, Tony.
'I thought it was blood. It was horrible!' he said.
'It wasn't until later I saw it was red paint.'

Tony shook his head.
'Somebody really wants you out of that flat!'

'Yeah,' said Matthew.

'They got the old chap in the flat next door yesterday.
The hospital said it was a heart attack
– but I'm not sure.'

'He had threats too, did he?'

'Some,' said Matthew.

'But when the new guy moved into the top flat
that was when things got really bad.
He plays music so loud that you can't think.
And he hammers at any time of day.
It drove the old man crazy.'

'It sounds as if the new guy's
part of the plan to get you out,' said Tony.

'You should go to the police.
You can't have people bullying you
and breaking into your flat.'

'I'll go to the police when I get some proof,'
said Matthew.

'And how are you going to get that?'

'I sprayed some stuff on my front door this morning.
Invisible ink. I made it myself years ago.
Nobody can see it but it turns purple on the skin.'

'So if anyone breaks into your flat,
their fingers will be purple?'
Matthew nodded. 'And they can't scrub it off!'
'Then let's hope,' said Tony,
'that it helps you to track them down.'

4

Threats at the Factory

The next day, Matthew phoned County Hall.

He needed to find out who owned Sandon House.

It turned out to be Barry Hogg.

Matthew had heard of him.

He had been in the paper last year.

He had tried to bribe someone in a land deal.

So Barry Hogg was behind it all!

That afternoon, Tony called Matthew into his office.

'I've just had a phone call,' Tony said.

'Somebody's threatening me.

Some guy rang, he said he'd ruin my business.'

Matthew could hardly believe it.

'Why would he do that?'

'It's simple,' said Tony. 'He wants me to sack you.'

'But why?'

'To get you out of Sandon House.'

'I don't understand,' said Matthew.

'How will sacking me get me out?'

'If you lost this job you'd have to leave town.

There's no work for you round here, is there?'

'No. I'd have to move south.'

'Exactly!' said Tony.

'Somebody wants to get you out of that building.

My bet is that they want to sell

that big piece of land behind the flats.'

'I know,' said Matthew.

'There's room for a supermarket.

But they need to knock down the flats

to make an access road.

Somebody would pay a lot for it.'

'That must be it!' said Tony.

'You're the last person left.

As soon as you go, they can get rid of Sandon House.

Then they can build the road and the supermarket.

They'd make a fortune!'

Tony was mad.

'Well,' he said. 'They're not going to bully me!'

Before Matthew could answer, there was a loud crash.

They jumped to their feet and ran out of the office.

A window had been smashed.

There on the factory floor was a brick

with a piece of paper tied round it.

Matthew picked it up and unfolded the paper.

5

The Men
in the Van

All day,
Matthew tried hard not to think about the note.
Tony had telephoned the police
but they weren't interested in a broken window.
Kids could have done it, they said.
Just for a laugh.

Matthew was sick with worry
and went outside for some fresh air.
As he walked into the yard,
a white transit van pulled up.

'We've come to do the window, mate,'
a man shouted from the cab. 'Is the boss around?'

Matthew went over to talk to him,
but stopped suddenly.
There was something on the man's hand.
Matthew stared. He couldn't believe it.
The man's fingers were purple.
It was the ink!

His heart was thumping.

'I'll go and tell the boss you're here,' he said.

'Won't be a sec.'

He ran back to the factory.

Tony was in the office. Matthew went in.

'The men have come with the glass,' he said.

'They're in the yard.

And one of them has my ink on his hands.'

Tony's mouth fell open.

'The stuff you sprayed on the door?'

'Yes. He must have broken into my flat yesterday.'

For a moment, Tony was silent.

'So they're not here to mend the window,'

he said at last.

'I bet they're planning to break in

– to steal the computers or something.'

Tony paused, then said

'OK Matthew, I've got an idea.

We can't let these yobs beat us.

Come over here . . .'

6

The Plan

At four o'clock, the phone rang in the office.

'It was another threat,'

Tony told Matthew later.

'They thought the broken window would scare me.

But I told them to get lost.'

Matthew nodded.

'Then we go ahead with the plan?'

'Dead right we do!'

When everybody had left the factory that night,
Matthew went and got the invisible ink.
'We'll spray it on the computers and the fax machine,'
said Tony.
'Those are the things they'll want to take.'

They covered each machine with the invisible ink.
They left nothing to chance.
They had made their plan.
They would stay at the factory every night.
They would watch and wait.

'We'll do nothing risky,' said Tony.
'If anyone breaks in, we'll contact the police.
We can use a mobile.'
'Right,' said Matthew. 'Sounds like a good idea.'

Tony dragged a chair into the store cupboard.
'I'll do the first shift,' he said.
'You go home and get some sleep.'
Matthew agreed to come back at two o'clock.
'We'll swap over,' he said.
'Then you can go home.'

When Matthew left, Tony switched the light off.
His chair was comfortable
and the cupboard was warm.
Before long, he fell deeply asleep.

It was several hours later when Tony woke with a start.
Torchlight was flashed in his face
and he felt the hard grip of a hand across his mouth.
'Don't try anything!' a man said.
Tony tried to get free.
But no! There were three men holding him down.
He could hardly breathe
and they dragged him across the floor.

'Put him over here, Kev,' said the same voice.
'Make sure he can't get away.'
Cloth was wrapped round his mouth.
Flex tightly round his wrists and ankles.
It was cutting into his flesh.
Tony felt sick with fear.
'What are we going to do with him?' one man asked.
'We'll dump him!' said another.
Then everything went black.

7

Trouble

At one-thirty, Matthew's alarm woke him.
He groaned.
Then he turned over and went back to sleep.

When he opened his eyes for the second time,
it was an hour later.

'I'm late!' he yelled. 'I should be at the factory!'
He jumped out of bed,
grabbed his jeans and raced out of the flat.

He got into his car and took off at top speed.
As he turned into Denning Street where the factory
was, he gasped.
Through the darkness and the drizzle
he could see the white transit van.

'They're here!' he said to himself.
'Those yobs will be taking anything
they can get their hands on.
And what's happened to Tony?'

With shaking hands, he called the police on his mobile.
'Hurry,' he said. 'Get here as fast as you can.
There's a break-in at the Denning Street factory.
My boss is inside.'

Matthew put the phone in his pocket.
He found a hiding place behind a waste bin
and prayed the police would come quickly.
But they did not.

Then, to his horror, he saw the three men
coming out of the factory.

They were carrying computers
and putting them into the van.
Matthew broke out in a sweat.
If the police didn't arrive soon,
the men would be gone.

He heard the slam of the van doors.
The engine started up.
The van began to move towards the gates.
It was dark, but as the van passed a street light
the number plate was clear.
Matthew could see it!
'Yes!' he yelled and pulled some paper from his pocket.
He wrote the number down,
then he ran across the yard into the factory.

'Tony!' he shouted. 'Tony! Are you all right?'
He ran through the factory to the office.

Tony was lying on the floor.
Bound and gagged. Still as a stone.
Matthew began to untie the cloth around his mouth.
As he did, he heard the sound of a police siren.

8

Police Success

Tony was lucky.

He only had a few bruises.

Even so, he spent the rest of the night at the hospital.

The next morning,

Matthew came to take him to the police station.

'Can you face the police, do you think?'

he asked as he helped him into the car.

'I'll gladly talk,' Tony said,

'if it means catching that lot.'

At the police station,

the Inspector took them to the interview room.

'You'll be pleased to know,' he said,

'we've caught all three of the thugs.'

'That's brilliant!' said Matthew. 'How did you do it?'

'We traced the owner of the van first,' he said.

'That was easy. You'd got the number, after all.'

'What about the other two?' asked Matthew.

'We guessed who they might be.

The van owner's mates are well known to us.

So we went to their homes but

– surprise, surprise! – they had alibis.

They said they had proof they were at a card game

when the robbery took place.'

Matthew looked across at Tony.

They were puzzled.

'Then how will you prove they did it?' asked Tony.

'It's simple,' the Inspector said.

'They had purple fingers.

Thanks to the invisible ink,

we've got all the proof we need.'

Matthew leaned forward.

'Was one of the gang called Barry Hogg?' he asked.

'Barry Hogg?'

The Inspector shook his head. 'No one by that name.'

Matthew couldn't understand it. It bothered him.

'If Barry Hogg wasn't one of the gang,'

he said to Tony as they left the station,

'how does he fit in?'

'Don't think about it,'

said Tony as he climbed into the car.

'Take a couple of days off work. You deserve a break.'

'Thanks!' said Matthew. 'It'll be good to get away.

I'll go up to the lake and do a bit of fishing!'

9

Still Shouting

Matthew returned to the flat.
He found his fishing rod
and put some warm sweaters into his bag.
Suddenly he noticed the electric fire had gone out.
'Fuse!' he said. But then he had a thought.
He tried the lights and checked the fridge.
Nothing.
'So the Bully Boy's cut off the power, has he?'
Matthew said.
'Stuff him! He's not going to get to me!'
Then he left the flat, slamming the door behind him.

He walked down the hall.

He was about to go through the front door
when the shouting started.

It was a man's voice coming from the lift shaft.

'Don't waste your breath!' Matthew called back.
'You won't bother me. I'm off!'

The yelling continued but Matthew didn't wait.

He'd had enough noise in Sandon House.

For the next few days,
he was going to have some peace and quiet.

10

Accidental Justice

Barry Hogg's throat was sore from shouting.
He had been trapped in the lift
in Sandon House for over an hour.
He was sick with worry.
His plan for the land deal was ruined.
Just one more week
and he would have bulldozed the flats
and signed the contract.
Now, he was finished.

Last night, Kevin had been caught at the factory.
He was sure to tell the police everything.
He had to get out of the country – fast!

He shouted again
and banged on the walls of the lift.
It was useless. Nobody came.
How long would this power cut last, he wondered.
Then a thought struck him
and a cold shiver ran down his spine.
Maybe it wasn't a power cut.
Maybe he had told the electricity company
the wrong date to cut off the power.
He was always getting dates mixed up.
What a fool!

He held his head in his hands.
And if he had told the electricity company
the wrong date ...
what had he told the demolition men?

The answer came minutes later.
A huge metal ball crashed against the front wall.
Red dust filled the lift shaft.
Brickwork began to crumble.
Then the lift began to shudder violently
before it made its long and final drop.